I Can Read...
Beauty and the Beast

Once upon a time, there was a merchant
who had three daughters.
The youngest daughter was called
Beauty. They all lived in the country.
One day the merchant had to go into
the town.
Beauty asked her father to bring her
a pink rose.

Beauty asked her father to bring
her a pink rose.

The merchant went to town.
The merchant got lost in the woods.
The merchant found a huge, old castle.
He went inside.

The merchant got lost in the woods.

There was no one in the castle. But there
was dinner on the table and a warm fire.
The merchant ate the food and went
to sleep.
When he woke up, he remembered that
he had promised to take Beauty a rose.

There was no one in the castle.

The merchant went into the garden
of the castle. He picked a pink rose.
The merchant heard a loud roar.
He saw a huge, ugly beast.
"That is my rose!" said the Beast.

The merchant heard a loud roar.

The merchant said he was sorry.
He explained that the rose was a present
for Beauty.
"I will spare your life if Beauty will
come and live with me," said the Beast.

The merchant said he was sorry.

When the merchant got home he told
Beauty what had happened.
Beauty said she would go and live
in the castle.
When Beauty met the Beast she
was surprised.
He was kind to her. Beauty and the
Beast soon became friends.

Beauty and the Beast soon
became friends.

Beauty missed her father and sisters.
The Beast said she could go home.
Beauty promised she would only stay at
home for a week.
But Beauty liked being at home so
much, she forgot her promise.
Beauty did not go back to the castle.

Beauty did not go back to the castle.

One night, Beauty had a dream.
Beauty dreamed that the Beast was
very ill.
She hurried back to the castle.
The Beast was dying of a broken heart
because he missed Beauty so much.

Beauty dreamed that the Beast
was very ill.

Beauty realised she loved the Beast.
She started to cry. Her tears fell on the
Beast's face. WHOOSH!
The Beast was changed into a
handsome Prince.

The Beast was changed into
a handsome Prince.

The Prince explained that a wicked fairy
had put a spell on him. The spell turned the
Prince into the Beast.
Beauty's tears had broken the spell.
Beauty and the Prince fell in love.
They lived happily ever after in the castle.